This book belongs to:

....

The Tooth Fairy's Visit

Chloe's tooth had been wobbling for ages. One day, as she was
jumping in and out of the fairy ring, at the bottom of the garden, the
tooth fell out. "Yes!" cried Chloe. "I've lost my first tooth at last!"
Chloe ran inside to show her mum.

"Put your tooth in here," said Mum, handing Chloe a sparkly pouch. "The Tooth Fairy will come in the night. She'll wave her magic wand over the bag and leave a special surprise."

That night, Chloe slipped the pouch under her pillow and fell asleep. As the clock struck midnight, she heard a tinkling noise. Right in front of her was a real fairy.

"I'm the Tooth Fairy," she said, waving her wand and taking
the special pouch. There was a shower of sparkles.
Suddenly, Chloe was in the garden and surrounded by fairies!

One fairy, with golden hair, took Chloe by the hand and
danced with her. The other fairies sang in sweet voices.
Chloe giggled as she danced round in circles.

The fairies flew about busily and Chloe looked up
to see them making a magical feast. There were yummy
cakes, delicious cookies and lots of other treats.

Chloe and the fairies had so much
fun eating all the tasty fairy food.

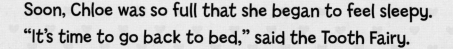

Soon, Chloe was so full that she began to feel sleepy.
"It's time to go back to bed," said the Tooth Fairy.

Back in Chloe's bedroom,
the fairy smiled and pinged
her wand over the pouch.
Chloe thanked the Tooth Fairy
and snuggled down to sleep.

The next morning, Chloe woke up and reached under her
pillow for the pouch. The tooth had gone!
In its place was a golden coin.

Chloe rushed downstairs to show her mum.
"I told you there would be a magical surprise,"
said Mum. "Next time one of your teeth
falls out, you'll know exactly what to do."

Chloe gave her mum a big hug.
"Thanks, Mum," she cried.
"You're the best!"

Mermaid Friends

Megan was very excited. Her friends were coming over to have a
mermaid party in the garden. Megan went outside to fill the paddling
pool with water, but she felt a spot of rain on her cheek.

"Mummy, it's raining outside!" cried Megan. She looked at her special mermaid outfit and began to cry. "Don't worry," said Mum, coming to see what all the fuss was about. "You can still play your game. I'll help you to set it up in the living room instead."

Mum went upstairs and brought down a patterned blanket and some sea-green scarves. She put them on the sofa, then pinned on pictures of starfish and bright fish. "It's a coral reef!" said Megan, smiling.

Next, Mum decorated the sideboard with her collection of crystals.
In the middle, she placed a glitter lamp, then arranged sparkly hair clips,
hairbrushes and mirrors all around it. The lamp lit up the room and
created silvery shadows, just like water ripples.

"What about the rock pool?" asked Megan.
Mum suggested they use Megan's old baby bath.
She filled it up with water, then dropped
in plastic fish, sponges and purple
bath salts. It was perfect!

Megan changed into her special mermaid outfit. As she twirled in front of the mirror, the glistening mermaid dress shimmered and twinkled.

Just then, the doorbell rang.
Ding-dong! "Hello, Suzy.
Hello, Bella and Pip," said Megan.
"Welcome to my mermaid party!"

Megan and her friends had so much fun playing in their enchanted, magical mermaid world. Megan and Suzy gently splashed in the rock pool, while Bella and Pip chatted on the coral reef and sang mermaid songs.